EDVARD GRIEG

(1843-1907)

Selected LYRIC PIECES
FOR THE PIANO

Compiled and Edited by Keith Snell

kjos   NEIL A. KJOS MUSIC COMPANY • PUBLISHER

EDVARD GRIEG
(1843 - 1907)
SELECTED LYRIC PIECES
FOR PIANO
Compiled and Edited by Keith Snell

CONTENTS

For supplementary study, a recording is available on compact disc, performed by pianist Diane Hidy (GP393CD). Ms. Hidy's interpretations follow this edition closely as a practical example for students.

ISBN 0-8497-6202-2

Edvard Grieg (1843-1907)

Edvard Grieg was born in Bergen, Norway. His great grandfather, Alexander Greig, emigrated to Norway from Scotland in 1765, and changed the spelling of the family name to Grieg. Grieg's Norwegian mother was a woman of musical cultivation who studied piano in Germany and England and played in public often before she married. It was from his mother that Grieg received his first instruction in music.

Norwegian violinist Ole Bull recognized Grieg's talent as a young pianist of 15. Bull persuaded Grieg's parents to enroll him in the Leipzig Conservatory. There he studied piano with E. F. Wenzel and Moscheles. Wenzel was a close friend of Robert Schumann, and imparted to Grieg an enthusiasm for Schumann's music. While attending a concert at the Gewandhaus, Grieg heard Clara Schumann perform Robert Schumann's *Concerto in A Minor*. This had a direct influence on Grieg in the writing of his own *Concerto in A Minor*.

In 1862, Grieg left the Conservatory and returned to Bergen where he gave a successful debut concert. The following year he went to Copenhagen to study with Niels Gade, a friend of Mendelssohn and Schumann and the leader of Scandinavia's Romantic school. In Copenhagen, Grieg met Nina Hagerup, a talented singer who eventually became Grieg's wife. She often performed Grieg's songs in her recitals.

A turning point for Grieg came in the year 1864 when he met composer Rikard Nordraak. Nordraak interested Grieg in Norwegian folksong as a source of musical material and inspiration. Grieg recognized the power and beauty inherent in his country's folk style and began to employ it constantly in his compositions. In 1866, Grieg performed in Christina, Sweden, a concert made up entirely of Norwegian music written by himself and Nordraak. The great success of this concert led to Grieg's acceptance as one of Norway's outstanding musicians. In 1868, the state of Christiana granted Grieg a financial subsidy to study and travel in Italy. In Rome, he met and played for the famous piano virtuoso Franz Liszt (1811-1886). Liszt played through Grieg's *Piano Concerto in A Minor* and praised it highly. In 1869, Grieg played the world premier of his Piano Concerto in Copenhagen. Thus, at the age of twenty-five, he established himself as a major composer of his time. The Norwegian government granted him an annuity which enabled him to devote most of his time to composition. Upon returning to Bergen, Grieg became the conductor of the Bergen Harmonic Society, a post he held for two years. An extensive European concert tour followed which reinforced his growing reputation throughout Europe.

In 1885, Grieg completed his permanent home in Troldhaugen, near Bergen, and for the next twenty years devoted his time to composing and touring. He received honors which included doctorates from Cambridge and Oxford and membership in the Institut de France. He submitted critical writing for foreign journals and worked to improve standards of criticism and performance throughout Norway. Despite his success, Grieg was of a retiring disposition and spent most of his later years at his house in Troldhaugen, avoiding visitors and shunning public acclaim. Six years before his death, his health began to fail. In 1907, he was preparing a tour to England but was ordered by his doctors to the hospital where he died. Grieg's death was mourned by all of Norway, and a state funeral was given in his honor. Grieg's remains were cremated, at his own request, and sealed in the side of a cliff projecting over the fjord at Troldhaugen.

LYRIC PIECES FOR PIANO

Grieg's entire creative life is exemplified by his sets of *Lyric Pieces* for piano. He composed ten sets of these pieces in thirty-four years, between 1867 and 1901. Grieg was at his best in short pieces, in which the perfection of form and the clarity of the musical line are remarkable. The combination of lyricism and nationalism led some critics to describe Grieg as the "Chopin of the North". Grieg's importance as a composer lies in the strongly pronounced nationalism of his music. Without resorting to literal quotation of Norwegian folk songs, he succeeded in re-creating their melodic and rhythmic flavor. The melodic expressiveness and contagious dance rhythms found in the *Lyric Pieces* impart a charm and individuality which has contributed to the lasting success of these rewarding compositions.

"It is not for me to build lofty places and mighty cathedrals of music,
but rather cottages, in which men may dwell and rest their hearts"

Edvard Grieg

NATIONAL SONG

Op. 12, No. 8

ELFIN DANCE

Op. 12, No. 4

WATCHMAN'S SONG

Op. 12, No. 3

Intermezzo
(Ghosts in the Night)

WALTZ

Op. 12, No. 2

GRANDMOTHER'S MINUET

Op. 68, No. 2

Allegretto grazioso e leggierissimo

SAILOR'S SONG

Op. 68, No. 1

ARIETTA

Op. 12, No. 1

Poco Andante e sostenuto

Puck

Op. 71, No. 3

Butterfly

Op. 43, No. 1

LITTLE BIRD

Op. 43, No. 4

Allegro leggiero

GADE

Op. 57, No. 2

Allegro grazioso

MARCH OF THE DWARFS

Op. 54, No. 3

D. C. al ⊕ Coda

NOTTURNO

Op. 54, No. 4

WEDDING DAY AT TROLDHAUGEN

Op. 65, No. 6

Tempo di Marcia un poco vivace